NOBODY WANTS
A NUCLEAR WAR

Nobody Wants a Nuclear War

Story and pictures by Judith Vigna

Albert Whitman & Company
Niles, Illinois

Other Books by Judith Vigna
Anyhow, I'm Glad I Tried
Couldn't We Have a Turtle Instead?
Daddy's New Baby
Everyone Goes as a Pumpkin
Grandma Without Me
Gregorio Y Sus Puntos
Gregory's Stitches
The Hiding House
The Little Boy Who Loved Dirt and
Almost Became a Superslob
She's Not My Real Mother

Library of Congress Cataloging-in-Publication Data

Vigna, Judith.
   Nobody wants a nuclear war.

   Summary: When a mother discovers her small daughter
and son have built a shelter to protect themselves
from nuclear attack, she explains that grownups all
over the world are working hard to make the world
safe for children to grow up in.
   1. Nuclear warfare—Juvenile literature.
[1. Nuclear warfare] I. Title.
U263.V54 1986 355'.0217   86-1654
ISBN 0-8075-5739-0

   The text of this book is printed in sixteen-point Janson.

Text and illustrations © 1986 by Judith Vigna
Published in 1986 by Albert Whitman & Company, Niles, Illinois
Published simultaneously in Canada by General Publishing, Limited, Toronto

For Kathy

Sometimes I'm scared there'll be a nuclear war and I'll never grow up.

"If there's a nuclear war," my brother told me,
"the whole world will blow up.
There'll be no more houses or trees
or animals or parents.
Only a dark, smoky desert
like we saw on television."

We thought we should build a hideaway,
just in case.
We went to the secret cave
in the woods behind our house.
We covered the opening with branches
so nobody would find us.

We smuggled in some cans of meatballs and soup
and filled some empty milk containers with water.
I brought the big snuggly picnic blanket
in case it got cold.

I felt safe.

Suddenly there was a loud crash,
and someone was shouting our names.
A bright white light flashed through the dark.
I thought the nuclear war had started.
We'd finished our hideaway just in time!

But it was only Mommy.
"We were making a hideaway
in case there's a nuclear war," I explained.

Mommy looked surprised. Then she hugged us.
"I know how scared you must feel," she said.
"Lots of children worry about nuclear war.
Grownups worry, too.
But you don't need to hide by yourselves.
Daddy and I will always try to be with you,
no matter what.
We care about you more than anything
else in the world."

Mommy talked more while we had lunch.
"In 1945, when Grandma was a young woman,
there was a kind of nuclear war.
It happened when the United States and Japan
were fighting in World War II.
The United States dropped an atomic bomb
on the city of Hiroshima in Japan.
The bomb brought an end to the war,
but the destruction it caused was more terrible
than anyone could have ever imagined.

"Later on, more countries started building nuclear bombs.
People worried that the bombs would be dropped.
There were air-raid drills in schools.
Children practiced hiding under their desks
in case a bomb fell.
One little girl was so scared by all this
that she thought she would never live to grow up.

"But some grownups were already working
to make sure an atomic bomb was never dropped again.
It hasn't happened,
and that little girl *did* grow up.
In fact, she now has children of her own.
I know, because that scared little girl was me."

Mommy says that lots of grownups all over the world
will never ever stop working to prevent nuclear war.
"People have different ideas
about how to solve the problem.
The president meets with people from many countries
to try to keep peace.

"Mr. Green next door writes letters to newspapers.
I belong to a group that sometimes has rallies.
We each work in our own way,
but we all have the same goal—
to make the world safer for you to grow up in."

I wanted to do something, too.
"I think we should make a great big banner," I said.

"Let's use the picnic blanket," Mommy suggested.
"We'll mail a picture of it to the president
so you can show him how you feel."

She found some scraps of material in her sewing basket.

I helped choose the words and put the letters in place.
My brother brought branches from our hideaway
to hold the blanket up.

When Daddy came home, we surprised him with our banner.
I asked Mr. Green to take our picture.
"We're going to mail it to the president," I told him.

I feel a little safer now.
I know Mommy and a lot of other grownups
are working hard so that there
will never be a nuclear war.
And I'll work hard
when I'm a grownup,
so my children can feel safer, too.